This book is dedicated to  to be mothers. May your very soon.

It is also for the courageous, and resilient women of my maternal lineage —my mother Yvaine, grandmother Lucienne, great-grandmother Anna, and beyond.

# Self Talk Love for Fertility

## On Your Way to Motherhood

Maryse Cardin

ISBN – 978-1-7751141-1-6

Book cover design by Avital David

Published by Dandelion Winds Press

**To learn more about the benefits of self-talk during the fertility journey:**
Visit Maryse Cardin at www.selftalklove.com or www.facebook.com/selftalklove

This book focuses exclusively on developing a loving, supportive, and kind inner voice during a woman's fertility journey. It does not provide any medical advice or information about fertility treatments. That's the job of medical doctors and health practitioners. I have no advice to provide in this regard as I am a communication teacher. Always seek the advice of your physician or other qualified health provider with any questions you may have regarding a medical condition. Never disregard professional medical advice or delay in seeking it because of something you have read in this book.

# Praise for Self-Talk Love for Fertility: On Your Way to Motherhood

**Joni Owen, Paediatric Nurse**
I finished your book in one sitting! Your book gave me a deeper understanding of what my moms have gone through. As I work in a high-risk hospital, I would say close to 80% of my clients have had miscarriages. I'll never forget the woman who had 11 miscarriages and on her 12th pregnancy, a healthy, beautiful baby girl. Such courage and strength.

Once again, the words written from your heart made me slow down and turn inward. (A very good thing which I need on a daily basis). The words in your book are comforting to women everywhere. We have lost the Red Tent. I and so many others are so very grateful to you, Maryse.

**Stefany Vendryes, Mom-to-be**
There are several points that have really resonated with me. There are a lot of really good points that I have started to practice in my own day to day. This is something that definetely helped and I really appreciate your thoughtfulness. I really think what you have written will help others too.
Thank you, thank you, thank you!

**Lori-Ann Speed**
Self Talk Love for Fertility is a tender book full of empathy and care. More than anything, this book will bring you the

comfort and love of a good friend combined with the transformative, sensitive and wise coaching of a medicine woman.

*Self Talk Love for Fertility* is intimate and personal, poetic and powerful. Intimate like you are having a heart to heart with your best friend or a cherished relative who loves you dearly.        Personal in that Maryse talks to you...directly to you in a personal and so soothing of a tone.  You feel seen, felt and understood.   It is filled with a poetic beauty; every word carefully chosen and placed. The self talk she offers is like magic balm for healing the many ouches on this journey. Powerfully positive and transformative, you can't read it without feeling seen, understood, reassured and calm.

Maryse offers kind words of wisdom and advice.  She shares positive stories that comfort and inform, inspire and uplift.   Her personal stories are beautifully honest and raw as are the stories of the other women going through the same process.

I highly recommend this book for the mother to be and for all those around her.  Without this book, it is difficult to understand or even imagine what the dear mother to be is going through and dealing with.  As a woman who did not have this challenge, my eyes have been opened and I feel a new tenderness and empathy for the sweet mothers to be going through this journey.   In fact, for anyone facing a challenge, this book can bring comfort and real tools of support in dealing with adversity.

# Table of contents

# Introduction

## Why I Wrote This Book for Mothers-To-Be

Trying to have a child when it doesn't come easy is the ultimate heroine's journey. It is a quest filled with love, longing, heartbreak, meaning, challenges, joy, and disappointments.

In a very real way, you leave the ordinary world behind. Once you are on this journey, your life becomes different from the billions of other women around the world who have children with ease. As you leave the world you know behind, you begin an adventure into an unknown place. You have to find your way through a maze of procedures, advice, medical assistance, and legal processes—and that doesn't even bring into play all the emotional strain of hope and loss and the complications of being in contact with other women who have children.

The heroine's fertility journey is not for the faint of heart. It is for those with big, brave hearts filled to the brim with love for that little being still to come.

The journey is challenging, however long it ends up being. It will put everything you know into question. It will shake up all of your relationships, including the one with yourself. There is an incredible transformation that takes place in the spirit, mind, and body of everyone who undertakes the journey. You will never be the same person again. I never was—and I say that in a good way.

You need tons of support, guidance, protection, compassion, and kindness during this time in your life, and you can be the one providing a big chunk of it to yourself with your self-talk.

Your inner self can become a safe harbour during this time; a place where you can take refuge, where you can be understood, where you will be loved, where you will be spoken to like a good mother speaks to her child. For make no mistake: You are more important than this journey. You are more important than your desire to become a mother. You are more important than your setbacks. You, my sweet, are so extremely precious.

It is during difficult times—whether a hard day or a total crisis—that we are most in need of help, support, and love from our own selves.

Your inner speech can work for you or against you during your journey. It can support you, make you more courageous and peaceful. It can be life-affirming, or it can be life-denying. It can stress you out, make you want to quit, and push you even deeper into the difficult feelings that many of us encounter on the way.

Ask yourself if your self-talk helps you cope with the lows of the fertility journey, or if it further distresses you. Does your inner speech provide you with support, compassion, and guidance during the inevitable dark days, or does it blame and attack you?

You are the one who listens to the voices inside you and you can choose which you will favour with your attention. Will you listen to the voice that says that something is wrong with you? Or will you listen to the voice that is kind and compassionate?

I have written this book because I was on this journey myself for about five years. At times it was so hard that it brought me to my knees. It broke me, but not like you think. As the author Elizabeth Lesser describes, it broke me open, like a flower that blooms, like a lotus sprouting from the mud. It was so hard that for the first time in my life it made me look inside and transform the relationship I have with myself. It put me on this path where I now have far more compassion, kindness, and love for myself.

You see, my fertility journey forced me to learn a new way to communicate with myself, to be with myself. I became so miserable during my own journey that I could not continue on like that. I became scared that I would stay that way no matter what the outcome. This misery became a huge motivator to change. For the first time in my life, I wanted to change, and I was ready to do what it took.

In his book about stress, *Why Zebras Don't Get Ulcers*, Dr. Robert Sapolsky writes that really wanting to change starts a momentum. "… once you sincerely want to change, the mere act of making an effort can do wonders."

I sincerely wanted to change. I was ready to start a new practice where I didn't bully myself and constantly put myself down. I couldn't take it anymore. There had to be another way of being.

When you change your self-talk, you change your brain. You change your whole way of being. You even change your cells. Everything you say inside is heard by your cells through sound waves and sensory transmissions. They react according to what they hear. Imagine the effect that loving self-talk has on them!

Speaking to yourself with love has loads of benefits that can be helpful during this time in your life. Research shows that those who speak to themselves in a positive and kind way get to experience the following benefits:

- They feel less stress.
- They are more calm.
- They have stronger immune systems.
- They are, overall, more healthy.
- They sleep better.
- They are more resilient.
- They are better at finding creative solutions to problems.
- And, incredibly enough, they tend to have more positive outcomes in life and have more success.

This book is written in the hope that it will support mothers-to-be in their own heroine's journey. The intention is to help develop a loving, supportive, and kind way to speak to yourself while you are on this challenging path. Speaking to yourself with love may become a lifelong practice.

In this book, I tell stories about my own journey to motherhood and how I spoke to myself and what I discovered. Each chapter contains a reflection time for you to take the time and space to transform your self-talk if you choose. I have also included some passages from stories of other women who have had a child after struggling.

I hope that these stories bring you comfort, provide you with a new way to look at your life, give a few helpful tools, and help you open a crack (or a huge open door) into speaking to yourself with love.

I know what it is like to be on this path and my heart goes out to you. I sit here in my little attic office with sun rays shining through the window and send you much love and energy. My daughter is now seven years old, and there isn't a day that I don't feel a huge amount of gratitude and awe that she is now here.

I leave you for now with this Buddhist prayer taught to me by my Zen meditation teacher, Hoben:
May you be happy, may you be healthy, may you be peaceful, may you live with ease.
And may your most precious and loving dreams of motherhood come true, however that may happen.

Much love to you dear mom-to-be,

*Maryse*

# Chapter 1

## Unwaveringly Stand by Yourself as a Good Mother Would
### Choose self-talk of love and compassion

Wanting a child more than you have ever wanted anything in your life and experiencing challenges conceiving one is a rough place to be. I believe that this is one of the toughest breaks a woman can encounter.

You need compassion and kindness—and you can be the one to give yourself those gifts. Friends and family, even if well-meaning, don't always understand what you are going through. You can become the person who gives yourself unfaltering understanding, support, and loads of unconditional love. You can do that with your self-talk.

Becoming a mother to a little baby is also learning to become a mother to yourself—a mother who loves unconditionally and stands strong and solidly by her child. As you go through this, recognize it as a chance to become this kind of mother to yourself. A strong and conscientious mother has your back, holds the safety net for you, and makes you stronger and braver. She comforts you and enables you to go further than you can go on your own. A good mother loves her child as she is, she loves all of her, and she stands by her.

I have been learning to be this mother to myself. It started on my fertility journey and continues to this day. I try every day to give myself the love and compassion that I need, and the beauty of it is that the more loving and compassionate I am with myself, the more I am with others.

By doing this, I have become a safe harbour inside myself. I can go inside now for comfort, for understanding, and most crucially, for a love of my faults, mistakes, challenges, and all.

This time is tough. This time is hard. But it is much harder to go at it alone—and if you are not on your own side, you are basically going at it alone. Everybody needs a loving mother on their side.

In fact, why not start now this beautiful transformation where you become your own good and loving mother, where you stand by yourself?

I wanted to be a mom because I had so much love to share inside my heart. It had to start with me first.

**My self-talk**

- I love you as you are.
- I will stand by you no matter what.
- I will always love you.
- This is really hard. I will hold your hand every step of this journey.
- You will never ever EVER be alone. I am here.

- I can see how hard this is for you. I can see how much you suffer and how much you want to become a mom. I understand. I really do.
- I can see that this is really taking a toll on you. I am here for you. I will care for you.

## A time for reflection

Do you think your self-talk could use a little self-compassion, a hint of mercy, and a bit of tenderness during this quest to motherhood? Self-compassion is to give yourself sympathy and tenderness for your hardships—no matter what they are, or who or what is causing them.

Imagine that your own daughter was going through a tough fertility journey of her own. How would you be with her? Would you stand by her? Would you love her through it? Would you remind her every day that she was not alone?

Now turn this light, this love, towards your own self.
Write the words that you would say to her. Then give them to yourself as a gift of love and compassion.

# Chapter 2

## Self-Talk Love Has No Conditions Attached: It Is Right Now
### Choose self-talk that celebrates how precious you are

You don't have to do anything special to deserve your own words of kindness and love. You don't have to be pregnant or already be a mother to be worthy of self-care. You don't have to be more successful or more beautiful to deserve inner words that are compassionate. You don't have to be so-called perfect to be worthy of a voice inside that is gentle with you, is filled with reverence, and treats you as the precious person you are. You don't have to be anyone other than who you are right now, at this point in your life, in the middle of your fertility journey, to deserve love.

At any moment—like this one right now—you can choose to speak to yourself with kindness, love, and compassion. No matter what you have said to yourself before, you can choose right now to elevate yourself with your self-talk. No matter what you have done, or what's been done to you, you can choose right now to start self-talk love.

You need this love now, and you will need it when you are on the other side of the journey—whatever that looks like for you. Some of the hardest times I have faced in my life were after I became a mother. Granted, nothing was as hard as my fertility journey, but there were days, weeks, and even long months that were very painful. I know several women for whom this is true, too. Becoming a mom didn't solve everything else.

My self-talk love is one of the practices that brings me back to a state of health, calm, joy, forgiveness, and equilibrium when times are tough. I learned these skills during my fertility journey and I now use them every day.

You have the power to reset your self-talk at any time. It can start now!

**My self-talk**

- You are a beautiful, amazing woman. I love you.

- I am here for you every step of the way.

- You are deserving of care and love.

- Your life has meaning.

- I love you just the way you are. You don't have to be perfect or change for me to love you.

**A time for reflection**

Are you waiting to start taking care of yourself? Are you waiting to start giving yourself the life-affirming words of love that are your birthright? I invite you here to take a few moments to think about what self-talk love would look like for you right now—no conditions attached.

# Chapter 3

# Give Yourself Freedom From the Inner Critic
## Choose self-talk that protects you from the negative voice

Becoming a loving and strong mother also means keeping yourself safe from any overly negative or cruel inner voices that may be attacking or criticizing you. It is your birthright to have protection, to stand up for yourself, to tell this voice to stop it. You can decide that the space inside of you is a place where bullying is not allowed. You can challenge the inner critic and learn to have some freedom from it.

This struggle to conceive is made so much harder if you go through it with a voice inside who ignores your needs, criticizes you, bullies you, and pushes you mercilessly to an end result without taking notice of what it is doing to you.

I once let this inside bully say whatever she wanted to say to me. This is just a glimpse of what the inner critic said to me during my fertility journey:
- There is something wrong with you.
- You will never be a mom.
- This will never work.
- You don't deserve to be a mom.

- You don't deserve to have what other women have.
- There is something wrong with your body.
- You have wasted your life.
- This is your fault.
- I am so ashamed.
- You waited too long.
- You wasted your time on unhealthy relationships and bad choices and now it is too late.

At a time when I was so in need of compassion and kindness, I was cruel and merciless to myself. I let the inner bully have a field day with me. I did not courageously come to my own defence.

Now that I know how speaking to myself cruelly affects me, when I catch the bully speaking to me that way, I stop her in her tracks. I stop listening to her. Then I give myself words that elevate me and give me love.

**My self-talk**
- What you say is not true. I don't believe you.
- Enough now.
- I know I am a good person. I am deserving of love and motherhood.
- Stop it. You don't know what you are talking about.
- I will not listen to you anymore.

**A time for reflection**

I am often asked how I am able to catch myself when my self-talk is negative or life-denying. This is how I do it.

I wait for a signal. A signal is a negative feeling or sensation of discomfort in my body. When I get one, I pay attention to what I am saying inside at that moment. I take stock. Getting a signal means that my self-talk is negative, or life-denying.

I first respond to the signal by telling that voice to stop. I come to my own defence like I would for a friend.

Then I bring myself comfort and give myself love. I tell myself the opposite of what the negative voice was saying to me. If it said that I am ugly, I say that I am beautiful in and out, and worthy of love. If it said that I am incapable, I say that I can do it and that I am guided. I replace the ugly words with words that are loving, kind, and supportive.

I make that choice over and over again, day after day.

Would you like to try coming to your own defence and then giving yourself comfort and love? It is possible for you to do it, too.

# Chapter 4

# Focus on What's in Your Power
## Choose self-talk to help discern what you can and can't control

My whole life, it seemed like I could achieve what I wanted by working harder. If I wanted something, I worked hard to get it and often did. I built a successful PR agency by putting in more hours, I laboured through graduate school, and when my relationships failed, I picked a different kind of man and built a solid, sustainable relationship. It seemed like a lot was in my control.

And then, bam! That illusion was shattered. No matter how hard I tried, I could not make a baby. Once I did make a baby, I could not keep it from miscarrying, and then, yet again, I could not make another baby for the longest time.

It was the first time that I realized that some things were totally out of my control. It was shocking and painful to realize that I just couldn't make this happen.

I am not the only one to realize it the hard way. Psychologist Dr. Martha Diamond, of the Center Reproductive Psychology, writes of the women who come for counselling:

"These patients are often highly successful people, and this is often the first time in life they are faced with the fact that hard work and being a good person doesn't result in success. I focus on the idea that conception is not a skill, and infertility does not define who they are as people."

As the Greek philosopher Epictetus wrote, we do not choose the role we are given in life, but only how we decide to play it. Some things are in our control, and others are not. It is to our benefit to know the difference.

It was not in my control whether I became pregnant or brought a baby to term, but the following WAS in my control:

- My decision to continue on this journey—I had the freedom every day to decide, over and over again, if I would continue trying to become a mom

- The practices that I did to feel peaceful and be healthy

- The way I spoke to myself and supported myself through this journey

- The people I surrounded myself with

- The nutritious food I ate

- How I sought professional help, like acupuncture or fertility specialists

- How I guided myself

- The meaning I gave to my life and to my journey to motherhood

- All of the choices that I made

**My self-talk**

- I focus on what I can control and let the rest be.

- There is a lot that is in my control.

- I trust myself.

- I am doing everything that I possibly can.

- I am powerful and make choices that support my dream.

**A time for reflection**

I invite you here to examine what is in your control during this journey to motherhood.

Make a list of all of the things that are in your control and all of the positive things that you can do to support yourself during this time. You are powerful and can make so many choices that support your dream.

Writing this list is telling yourself about how much power you do have and how many wonderful things you are doing to move towards your dream of motherhood. It can make you feel like you do have some control and make you grateful for what you are doing.

# Dr. Alda's story

Dr. Alda Ngo is a doctor of acupuncture, specializing in fertility. She went through her own fertility struggles, even as she helped her patients with theirs. It took her seven years and she suffered two miscarriages before her son came along. He is now a happy and healthy four-year-old. Here are her words:

It was an intense time. Fertility struggles were everywhere for me, in my work life and in my personal life.

It was not alienating or isolating as it can be for so many women. It was very therapeutic in some ways.

Sometimes, it was hard and sad, like when I had a miscarriage. I was sad and I was around other women who were sad all day.

I was very present in how I dealt with it. I needed a lot of personal space.

I sought refuge in my meditation practice and in my community, also in my fertility doctor and my colleagues.

The unknown was difficult. I had so many strong emotions: the sadness, the anger, the grief of longing for something that is not happening, and not knowing if it would happen one day.

For many of us, coming to acupuncture is empowering. It is natural. It gets you in tune with your body and you are in a supportive environment. It helps you be as healthy as you can in body, spirit, and mind.

I hold the space in a certain way for my patients. I validate their feelings.

The majority of my patients will become moms if they really want it. The question is: by what means. If you really know what you want, you keep going. I have met with some of the children my clients adopted, or had naturally, with donor eggs, or with IVF—and each child was precious and I felt a connection to them.

For me, it was learning how to be ok with not being in control. Like: how do I do IVF and be relaxed? How do I let go of outcome with trust, acceptance, and peace while still trying to make it happen—it was that sweet spot in between.

During the hardest time after my miscarriage, I went on a meditation retreat with Thich Nhat Hanh. For me he is like a living Buddha—he embodies love and peace. We were told that we could ask one question of him. I stayed up all night composing my question. When it was my turn, I asked him about what to do and told him how difficult it was for me trying to have a child and also to be there for my patients. He looked at me with eyes of total love and compassion. He said there would be a lot of people who would look at my life and see all that I have and how I have so many conditions for happiness.

29

A sense of gratitude and wonder came over me. It's like I changed the channel. After that, each time I felt sad, like when my period came, the sadness was a reminder that I already have so many conditions to be happy.

# Chapter 5

# Following My Own Fertility Path Map
## Choose self-talk for guidance and inspiration

I came home completely crushed from the birthday party of my friend's little daughter. I had spent the morning surrounded by small children and pregnant women, and wasn't out of her house more than a few seconds before I burst into tears. When I got home, I felt so low. My self-talk was super negative, super life-denying. It sounded like this:

- You will never be a mom.
- This will never work.
- You are unworthy of being a mom.
- You can't have what all those other women have.
- There is something wrong with you.
- There is something wrong with your body.

I needed some self-talk love. I also needed guidance because I felt lost. Quickly, I went to my desk and opened up my notebook, where I kept my Path Map. I looked at it and drew reassurance from it. I could see, at a glance, exactly where I was. The next week, I would be having a procedure to remove scar tissue from my uterus, increasing the likelihood that I would get pregnant. I told myself:

- It is all going well.
- Keep going. You will get there.
- There are still many steps to be taken.

- Everything is ok.
- I love you.
- Your life looks nothing like theirs, but you will be a mom too.

Like someone about to be swept away in a tsunami of despair, I needed someone to help me secure my footing, to keep me on dry land, to grab my hand and pull me back to safety. I did that for myself that day with my Fertility Path Map and my positive and loving self-talk.

A map shows you a way forward. The route doesn't have to be set in stone, but with your map, you'll have a direction to go. Writing that map for yourself lets you relax a little. If I was having a sad or stressful day, I would look at the map I had written and draw comfort from it, as I would know that I was exactly where I was meant to be. I could be reassured that I was headed in the right direction.

A map is a great visual way to communicate with yourself. It brings all the parts of you up to speed with what you are trying to achieve. My map helped me to keep my direction, and also provided comfort when I needed it. It gave me clarity and focus. It helped me to not feel lost.

**My self-talk**

- You can do this.
- Keep going step by step on your own path.
- I know we will find a solution.

- Follow the map for now. You are headed in the right direction.
- Everything is going according to plan.

## A time for reflection

Would you like to create your own Fertility Path Map? I made my map very visual so that I could see where I was at a glance. It had circles and arrows and was in colour. It also included some positive and loving self-talk.

Write down all of the steps you can think of in this journey. You can change and add anything you want to your map; it is a road mark for you. You can also add some loving and encouraging self-talk to your map. Add lots of colour if you are inspired.

# Chapter 6

# Beauty in What Is
## Choose self-talk to celebrate the good in this journey

The fertility journey can be a hard, stressful task. It's like climbing a steep mountain at times but is made even worse by not knowing when you will reach the summit. It is filled with pain, tears, fear, and confusion (that is for sure), but there can also be great beauty in it, just like the views you could enjoy while climbing that mountain.

Make no mistake—I could write a very long list of all that was ugly, painful, unfair, devastating, and hard, but that's not the entire picture. There was a lot that was beautiful, nurturing, encouraging, loving, and life-affirming during this time. It's in my power to decide what I want to focus on and what I want to say to myself. Without dishonouring the complexity of all my feelings, I can choose to see beauty, too.

This is where I saw beauty in my own journey:
- For the first time in my life, I put myself first. I decided that I was important enough, and that my dream was important enough, to make myself and my child-to-be my very first priority. For the first time, I honoured myself and my feelings.

- I started talking to myself with love and compassion.

- I showed resilience and determination. I left no stone unturned. If I heard that something could help, I did it—from fertility yoga to weekly acupuncture appointments.

- I had always somewhat admired individuals who meditate. I liked the idea of meditation, but I thought I wasn't capable of sitting still. It turns out that I really like sitting still and being quiet. It does me good. I became one of those individuals who meditate. Sitting on my meditation cushion makes me feel calmer, no matter what state I am in.

- I took really good care of myself. I ate better than ever, got lots of sleep, and did some form of movement every day. I lost weight and became more healthy and fit. I felt good in my body. I even healed my long-held lower back pain and chronic constipation. Sometimes I made mistakes and tripped up, drinking too much wine or becoming overly stressed, but I tried to be forgiving and kind to myself about it, and then to very gently come back to my self-care.

- Even amidst this challenge, I found some peace inside myself for the very first time as I went deeper into myself than I ever had before. I discovered that there's a place inside of me that is untouched, that is good, that is calm.

- I hurt so much at times that I finally surrendered. I recognized that this was bigger than me and that, for the first time, I couldn't put more effort into making something happen. I had to find a way to let it be what it was while still moving towards my dream. I started thinking about what it means to be satisfied with what I have, while still wanting more.

- My husband stayed committed in his support of me. He was there with me every step of the way—even in the hard times. He showed me that he was in for better or for worse, from holding me when I cried for hours to coming to all of my appointments. He even had acupuncture himself, even though he isn't a big fan. This doesn't mean that we didn't have arguments or that there wasn't a lot of stress on the relationship, but we got through it together.

Trying to become a mom is what your life is about right now, so protect it. Honour it. Nourish it. Love yourself in it. See the beauty in what is, if you can.

**My self-talk**

- This is hard, but it is precious. It is my life. It is important.
- You are more important than your problems.

- I would like to say yes, but I need to say no. I just don't have the resources to do this right now.
- Maybe this is as good as it gets for now.
- You are doing your best. Just keep it up.
- Where can I find beauty here?
- What can I give thanks for today?

**A time for reflection**

Imagine telling yourself that it is okay, no matter what is happening; that you know you are doing your very best, and that is all that you can do. Give yourself permission to be who you are, and to feel what you do on your way to motherhood.

In this exercise, you are invited to write a message that reflects the beauty in your fertility journey.

# Chapter 7

# A Cat in the Sun
## Choose self-talk to calm and relax during this traumatic time

One day I told my therapist that I often felt stressed, worried, and anxious, and that being around certain people or doing certain things only made it worse. My wise therapist advised me that in order to increase my chances of success, I had to be like a cat in the sun, not like a cat hanging desperately from the drapes. He recommended that I try—as much as possible—to only expose myself to situations that made me feel like a cat in the sun. He suggested that I keep myself as relaxed as possible and avoid people and situations that increased my already-high stress levels. He said that fertility challenges were traumatic, and that I needed to make sure that I didn't put more pressure on my already-taxed nervous system.

In Unsung Lullabies: Understanding and Coping with Infertility, a team of clinical psychologists write:
"Infertility is a trauma because it attacks both the physical and emotional sense of self, it presents us with multiple, complicated losses, it affects our most important relationships and it shifts our sense of belonging in the world."

Being like a cat in the sun became a driving motto for me. I learned to honour myself and what I was going through. It was not business as usual in our home, it was a time when a lot of calm, healing, and nurturing was needed. When I suffered difficult setbacks, like getting my period, visiting yet another doctor, or going to the fertility clinic— oh, how stressful that was—I would make sure that I took the time and space to let my nervous system calm down.

I am a highly sensitive person. That means that my brain is wired to capture so much more information than 80 percent of the population. I am extra-aware of all kinds of subtleties, feelings, and sensations in my body. This extra load of stimuli makes my nervous system easily overstimulated. I need a lot of down time in order to feel calm and reduce the over-arousal in my body—and this is just on a normal day. During times of trauma, I need way more. That's why, for me, being like a cat in the sun was not just about achieving a pregnancy; it was also about remaining healthy and sane during the fertility journey.

Other people are wired differently than I am, as a highly sensitive person, and I came to accept and honour that. Some people can work full-time at very stressful jobs while they also try to become mothers and go through fertility treatments. I am not wired to be able to handle that level of stress in a healthy way. That's me, and I need to be me. For the first time, I gave myself permission to choose people and situations that brought me the most peace.

Being around calm people is calming for me. That's because there is a process called "entrainment," in which your body syncs up with the rhythms and beats of other people. I started going regularly to a meditation group because being around those people made me feel calmer, even if my own mind was racing when I arrived.

Being around people who are anxious and doing nothing about it has the opposite effect. Their anxiety is contagious to me. Anything or anyone that caused me to feel more anxiety had to be pushed aside or minimized for the time being. Some things and people naturally fell away.

**My self-talk**
- Let's stay at home. It is important that we rest.
- I am going to give myself the time I need to be alone and find my center again.
- I am feeling overwhelmed right now. I am going to take some time to calm down.
- I am going to help you calm down.
- Tell me about today. Let's sit here together quietly. I will listen to you.

**A time for reflection**
Can you imagine becoming like a cat in the sun? Yeah, I know, easier said than done. But what about heading in that general direction, taking steps that may lead there? Talk to yourself about that idea and the practices that you do—or would like to do—in order to foster a sense of calm within yourself.

# Chapter 8

## What Needs to be Released
### Choose self-talk to lovingly put yourself first

One of the subjects that are most frequently brought up in infertility support groups is the damage that this hardship causes to friendships and family. It's hard on everyone when you can't handle baby showers or meet with a friend who is now pregnant.

My own journey cost me three close friendships with women who were all pregnant. When I saw or spoke to them, I felt all of these strong feelings that I was embarrassed to admit; I was sad, I felt inferior to them, I was jealous, I felt stressed. I tried so hard to be happy for them, but I felt no happiness, just sorrow for myself. I lied and said that I did feel happy for them, and that made me feel worse and more alone. I tried to get over it, but I couldn't, so in the end, I decided to respect myself and my feelings. I could no longer keep hurting myself in that way. I thought of the words that my wise therapist had said about being like a cat in the sun, and I distanced myself from them.

Yet these women were important to me. I loved them. They had been close to me—all three had been at my wedding. They were good women. It was a hard decision to make and I would have rather not been in a position to have to make it, but I was. There came a point where, for maybe the first time in my life, I put myself and my family-to-be first. I needed all the energy I could muster to not just endure all this, but to prevail (to paraphrase William Faulkner).

It is common, during this journey, to have relationships fall away. In my experience, very few people understand what it is like unless they have been through it themselves. They may sympathize, but they don't understand the heartache of longing to be a mother. A difficult fertility journey does not only affect parents-to-be, it affects the people around them, too.

Even today, as I look back, I wouldn't change what I did, despite the fact that I still feel a lingering of guilt, and still miss these women in my life. One of my teachers, Gail Larsen, talks about having honourable endings, so it is with much gratitude that I think of those women now. I tell myself about how much their friendship meant to me and all the love we gave each other.

I also feel gratitude for our roads parting ways so that I could have enough courage, inner peace, and energy to continue on my own road.

**My self-talk**
- I will put your well-being first.
- It is important that you keep your strength and energy for this journey.
- I will not sacrifice you.
- You are important to me.
- Becoming a mom is my highest priority right now.

- Be as kind as you can with others while still honouring yourself.
- I let other people have their own feelings and their own methods of dealing with it.

**A time for reflection**
Is there anyone or anything that you feel you may have to let go of to help you on your journey? This can even be an old way of thinking that no longer serves you. Tell yourself about what you need.

If letting go is needed, think of the concept of an honourable ending. You can let go of things and of people with love and gratitude in your heart. You can thank them for their love and remember all that you have shared together. Then let them be, let them go. Some may be there at the end of the journey and others may not, but that is not up to you. One moment will naturally lead to the next and to the next. Right now, it is time to focus on your well-being, and on your family-to-be.

# Chapter 9

# A Time for Extreme Self-Care
## Choose self-talk for well-being

Having a child was huge for me, a quest of Olympic proportions. I wanted it more than anything I had ever wanted. I vowed to myself that I would leave no stone unturned and do everything I could to put the chances on my side. One of the ways I did this was to give myself permission to practice extreme self-care.

I didn't have a history of caring for myself. In fact, it was the opposite. Before the fertility journey, I ate a lot of takeout. I didn't sleep enough. I hardly ever exercised. I never took the time to touch base with my spirit. I worked long hours in a stressful job. I was 30 pounds overweight. My skin was always breaking out. I was chronically constipated. I also put the needs of others before mine.

Now, I took care of my body by eating well, getting lots of sleep, and exercising regularly and lightly. I also saw my acupuncturist every week and went to yoga. I lost weight and felt much stronger and lighter. I took care of my emotional well-being by surrounding myself with positivity. I only read, listened to, or watched things that would uplift me and that were nurturing. I dropped like hot potatoes favourite TV shows that were violent or upsetting.

As I've said before, I also cared for myself by minimizing exposure to people and situations that caused me too much stress. Instead, I surrounded myself with my very own circle of love: a few trusted individuals who could help and love me through this. With all of them, I felt safe. They helped me feel like a cat in the sun. I took care of my spirit with meditation, chanting, attending a retreat in a monastery, and praying. I also got help when I needed it. My fertility challenges brought up all kinds of stuff from my past, which I didn't know how to process. I also needed help healing from my miscarriage. I turned to a very kind and wise therapist to help me.

When I finally had the good fortune to get pregnant and bring a baby to term, I was feeling better than I had ever felt—despite how stressful that time was for me.

**My self-talk**
- It is important that I take the time to care for myself during this period.
- I take good care of myself.
- I give myself permission to care for myself.
- I am healthy and strong in all ways.
- I trust you.
- It is important that I surround myself with individuals who can hold the space for me.

**A time for reflection**
How are you caring for yourself during this time? Tell yourself all about how you are keeping yourself healthy and strong.

# Michelle's Story

Michelle Remillard is now mom to a healthy and happy 13-year-old boy. Here is her story and her words for you:

We tried for six months before going on an ovulation-inducing fertility drug. I was 34 years old. I became pregnant after the 3rd month on this fertility drug.

Taking the drug gave me hope that it would happen. At least my doctor was very positive.

I now know I have Lupus. (Lupus is a systemic autoimmune disease in which the body's immune system mistakenly attacks the body's healthy tissue.) But I was only diagnosed with this after my son's birth. If I would have known this prior, it might have been easier for me and my doctor. We could maybe have gone on fertility drugs earlier, but I am not sure.

I wish I hadn't blamed myself so much. There really was nothing extra I could have done.

I also wish I would have maybe done more for myself, such as get a massage/reflexology, and just chilled out. I would not try to get so many things done, like the meals and the housework, and my job.

I want women to know: don't lose faith. There are a lot of options out there. Get yourself a good doctor who you trust and can talk to. It's also nice to talk to other folks that are going through the same thing. Go on a vacation, somewhere where you just have a good time and not just focus so much on "why can't I get pregnant," and of course take your hubby, and a bottle of wine. :)

# Chapter 10

# The Morning I Looked Reality in the Face
## Choose self-talk of acceptance of your feelings and your circumstances

"This may not happen for you."

There it was, said out loud, by my therapist. I was shocked to hear it, and I wanted to deny it, but I knew it was real. I had been so terrified of admitting it to myself. "You know that, right?" he asked gently. I nodded yes as tears streamed down my face. I was scared and sad, but also relieved to hear the truth said out loud. I had been so scared that if I admitted that to myself, it would decrease the chances of succeeding, or I would get discouraged and give up. But not accepting reality made me feel even more scared and more nervous, like I was trying to outrun something.

Psychology Today has this to say about fighting reality:
"You are upset—understandably upset—about a difficult situation or some aspect of yourself. You angrily question how unfair life is or why you don't change. You fight the current situation, bringing on feelings of distress about your pain. This dilemma is so common that the Buddhists long ago reduced it to a formula: Pain × Resistance = Suffering. Translation: Fighting against (or resisting) the reality of the pain in your life creates suffering."

Accepting reality meant this for me:

- I was on a different path than other women. This was not business as usual. I could not do right now what others did. I had something else to do.
- Most people did not understand what I was going through.
- I needed a lot of self-care.
- This was really hard and painful.

It also meant accepting the reality of what I was feeling during this journey. I had such intense feelings of sadness, anger, despair, hope, jealousy, fear, and loneliness. I started letting myself feel all of these huge intense feelings. Some were difficult to deal with, but it was much easier than shoving them down. My therapist helped me deal with these feelings.

Accepting reality is not the same as becoming resigned, liking it, or stopping moving towards your dreams. It is not about giving up. In fact, living in reality gives you a platform from which to strive towards your dreams as you stand more solidly. When I accepted my reality, I could feel myself being more solid. I didn't like this reality, but I came to accept it and to see acceptance as a choice I could make. It took way less energy than rejecting it and keeping it at bay.

On one side I balanced the fervent intention that I would be a mom, and on the other side I lived with the reality that I was on a challenging fertility journey and didn't know how it would end. I realized that in my self-talk I could tell myself the truth, I could help myself feel my feelings, and I could help myself accept my reality, my truth.

**My self-talk**
- It is my birthright to have my own truth, to have my own feelings.
- I accept that this is my truth, even if I don't like it.
- I accept what I am feeling.
- I want to know what is true to me.
- I may not like what is happening, but I choose to accept it.
- I accept reality.
- This is a hard time. Yes, it is. Many, many women get through it and become mothers.

**A time for reflection**
I invite you here to choose to accept the reality of your circumstances or feelings.

Take a few moments to write about what is real and true to you. I got lots of help during my journey from my meditation teacher, my therapist, my fertility yoga teacher, and my acupuncturist. They helped me to keep going and also to look inside. I encourage you to get help, too, if you feel it can help you.

# Chapter 11

# This Is Not Your Fault, You are Innocent, My Love
## Choose self-talk that is without blame

When my daughter was a baby, I watched a few episodes of a TV show called Cupcake Girls. It was a reality show about two women who ran a chain of cupcake stores together. One of them was undergoing fertility treatments in real-time on the show.

I couldn't believe it. I sat there mesmerized as she brought a camera in with her to the offices of fertility specialists. I found her so open and honest. What especially fascinated me was the fact that she was willing to expose herself like that, and to potentially fail in front of an audience. (Spoiler alert: she got pregnant during the show.)

My own journey was lived in a cloud of secrecy. I told very few people about it. I felt deep shame at having trouble conceiving. I believed there was something defective about my body, about me, that there was something very wrong with me, and that I was a fraud. I also thought that if I failed, it would be worse if others knew about my pain, about my failure. I couldn't bear to have anyone feel sorry for me or to have to deal with their questions. I worried about upsetting others with all my intense feelings. I was living in limbo in another world, separate from theirs.

The whole thing felt shameful to me. I could not do what others did so easily. While others made babies with love and sexual passion, our journey involved peeing on sticks, schedules, crying over the return of my period every month, forced sex, clinics, procedures, collecting sperm samples, consultations with doctors, and surgeries. In addition, talking about fertility felt a little like talking about sex, and I couldn't handle that.

I have come to believe that this just compounded a shame that I felt about being a woman. I carried with me the embarrassment of many generations of women in my family who were not at ease with sex, menstruation, desire, passion, breastfeeding, or any other reminders of deep womanhood.

Sarah Fletcher—whose own journey to motherhood included an ectopic pregnancy before giving birth to two children—wrote this about the disgrace she felt:

"When I look back on that time, I still find it terribly sad that I believed it was my fault. I want to cry when my friends who have experienced infertility think the same. It's not their fault. It wasn't my fault… I have many friends who have struggled with fertility issues, but who are reluctant to talk about it to anyone. They feel ashamed. They think it's their fault. In some cases, even their own parents don't know what they've been through."

I wish I had known that most women on this journey felt the same as me. I wish I had known that it wasn't my fault. I wish I had really understood how traumatic this all was. I wish I had given way more compassion to myself as a woman who felt unworthy and ashamed.

It is so sad how many of us going through the fertility journey feel shame. Shame that our bodies don't work like those of other women, shame that we are not perfect. We keep it all hidden, like a dirty secret, like it's taboo. We are isolated, stripped away from many of life's simple joys, like enjoying the birth of a friend's baby.

But it doesn't have to be this way. The opposite of shame is love. We can be there for ourselves, proud of how strong we are, proud of carrying so much love for our child-to-be. With our self-talk, we can show ourselves that we are not alone.

So please remember, my love, that none of this is your fault. Whatever your age is, whatever you have done or not done in your life, whoever you are—it is not your fault that you are having challenges becoming a mother. You are completely innocent. It is just the way it is for now.

**My self-talk**
- I wish I had put my hand on my heart and said to myself:
- This is very, very hard. It is not your fault in any way.
- This is a very painful and difficult journey to be on. You are doing everything that you can.
- I love you very much.
- I will always stand by you.
- You are not alone.

- It is not your fault. It is not your fault. It is not your fault.
- There is no one to blame. You are innocent. This is just how it is.

## A time for reflection

I want you to know that this is not your fault; you are innocent, no matter what you have done in your life, and no matter how old you are. I invite you to let yourself know that it is really not your fault, that there is no reason at all to feel ashamed or disgraced. You are so, so, so deserving of love, compassion, and motherhood. It is your birthright. Take a moment with yourself to have this important and loving inner conversation. Put your hand on your heart for a fuller connection and really tell yourself that you are not to blame, that you are innocent. There is no one to blame. This is just how it is.

# Chapter 12

# You Are Not Alone to Live This Story
## Choose self-talk that connects you with your sisters on this path

Your story is not a new one. There have been women on this journey since the beginning of time. We are a sisterhood of women who want children so badly that we ache. From ancient times, this has been part of the lore— not the mainstream stories, for we are not mainstream, but a real story that is always present in every society, everywhere.

Stories have always been a way through which we make sense of ourselves and what it means to be human. Many cultures had myths and epic stories, about women who longed to be mothers. It goes back a long way. Many regions of the world have fertility goddesses that women have prayed to for thousands of years, such as the Egyptian Isis and the Nigerian Osun. On the Big Island of Hawaii, there is a sacred fertility rock where women have brought flowers since ancient times.

The Bible also contains several stories of women getting pregnant after wishing for motherhood for many years. One such story caught my attention and became an inspiration for me. It was the story of Elizabeth. The story goes like this:

Elizabeth was the cousin of Mary. Elizabeth and her husband, Zechariah, had tried for years to have a child, and she was now past the age where she thought that she still had a chance. I'm not sure what it meant, in those days, to be an older woman, but to put it in perspective, Mary was a teenager when she gave birth to Jesus.

Think about what it must have been like to have fertility challenges in a time when a woman's entire value was in giving her husband and community children. Imagine the pressure. There was not much fertility assistance in those days, and it was believed that a woman was barren because she was sinful. Ouch.

As Elizabeth grew older, she came to accept that she may not become a mother. She made peace with it. And then, unexpectedly, she discovered that she was pregnant.

Elizabeth was not just a mother, she was an older mother. Now *this* was a character I could relate to. She had struggled for years, she was now getting older, and yet, despite all this, she was to become pregnant and give birth. Elizabeth had a son. Not just any boy, mind you, but one who was to grow up and become John the Baptist, the cousin of Jesus.

I returned often to the story of Elizabeth during my fertility journey. I found meaning in her story. I could relate to her. She helped me keep believing that it was possible.

As the heroine of your own story, you get to choose the meaning that each person, event, and outcome holds in your life. With your self-talk, you can help yourself understand what your life is about. It's all up to you.

The story of Elizabeth helped me to understand my own story, and also to keep hope alive. If Elizabeth could accept the fact that she was childless, then so could I. If Elizabeth could continue living with dignity, strength, and faith, then so could I. If Elizabeth could have a child at a later age, then so could I. If she could have a child despite the odds, then so could I.

Elizabeth was a guide for me during that difficult period. I told myself her story over and over again. "You can survive too," I said to myself. "You can accept it too," I said to myself. "You can be lucky like her too," I said to myself.

During that time, I also read a travel memoir called *Travelling with Pomegranates*, written by a mother and her daughter. The two of them had travelled together to see divine feminine icons in Europe. The daughter, looking for guidance in her life, created her own trinity of role models, choosing Joan of Arc, Mother Mary, and Athena. They became guiding lights for her as she strove to understand her own life.

**My self-talk**
- I can become a mom, too.

- I can survive with dignity, grace, and love—whatever happens to me.
- This is meaningful to me. Becoming a mom is meaningful to me.
- I find meaning in the stories of others. I get to decide what this journey means to me.
- I am part of a larger sisterhood of women who have shared this journey.
- It is not what happens to me, it is what I decide to believe of it.
- My life is filled with meaning. I am guided.

**A time for reflection**

Sit down with yourself. Do you have a story of your own that inspires you? Are there any characters from myths, legends, or real life that can guide you with their qualities? Conduct some research, if you are so inclined, into a character who can serve as a guide for you.

- What is the story of that woman?
- What qualities does she have?
- How can you be/live like her?

# Laila's story

Laila Wong is now mom to a healthy and happy 9-year-old girl. Here is her story and her words for you:

We tried to conceive a baby for 14 years. Two years prior to that, we didn't really try to become pregnant, but we also didn't mind if we happened to get pregnant, so we didn't use birth control.

I didn't know how closely tied the loss of my fertility would be to my self-esteem. It was nothing but a big repeated failure with a lot of false hope all the time. So I wish I had known just how much of an awful impact it would have on my life at the time. It was only through egg donation that I could achieve a pregnancy.

It would have been better to be less stressed and busy all the time. I had to work full-time in those early years and I had to look after so many other things in life. In retrospect, I think I would have been much better off to take much more time to myself. This isn't possible for so many people.

I also wish I had talked to more people about what I was going through. Up until that point in life, I had pretty much achieved anything I had ever wanted, so not getting pregnant was a huge failure and I didn't know how to deal with the sense of failure. So, I kept it to myself and only shared with a few close friends who I don't think really understood. I worked in an organization that was full of supportive women, but I was in leadership, and I didn't feel it was right to share what I was going through, so I really suffered in silence a lot. I would cry all the way to work and then put on a stiff upper lip for the whole day. I did that all the time. Now I still work with supportive women and I have younger women who tell me what they are going through. As a leader to them, I can be really supportive and I am so happy that they are open about their fertility problems.

I also wish I had a better defence at the time to the many ideas and thoughts that people shared with me that were so not helpful! People love to tell you that you will get pregnant "if only you relax more, or if you start the adoption process, you will likely get pregnant while waiting." I found that many women didn't understand fertility struggles, and their comments were actually hurtful even though they didn't mean to be that way.

Having a supportive partner was very helpful and he always understood how much it meant to me and how badly I wanted a child. I think that my exercise regime was also very helpful as it was something that I could do well, and it made me feel better all the time. And, my work was actually helpful, as a distraction. If I hadn't had distractions, I likely would have been crazy from only focusing on something that I could not achieve.

I think it was also helpful to have a lot of friends who didn't have children, as we could begin to see that life without a child would have also been ok. But in the end, we were blessed, and it is now hard to remember all the difficult and awful times, thankfully.

# Chapter 13

# See it Happen, Feel it Happen
## Choose words that help you visualize your baby in your arms

I had a little secret the whole time, a little treasure that I kept in my wooden chest. I had a brown teddy bear called Charlie, a little wooden toy car, and an illustrated book about a red dog. These were items I had kept preciously to give to my child one day. When I looked at them, I connected with the joy, contentment, and amazement that I would feel one day when my child played with them. I saw her playing with them, and you know what? There came a time when my little daughter *did* play with them. Charlie was especially popular.

I made sure that many times a day, I lived in a future where I was a mom to a beautiful baby. I transported myself to a place on the other side of my fertility journey, a place in which I had been blessed by my most ardent desire: I was a mom. I visualized being a mom, and connected with the feeling of happiness, joy, and love that it would bring.

Visualizing our future is a powerful way that we communicate with ourselves. We paint a picture for ourselves, we show ourselves what the end goal is.

In her epic book on the topic, *Creative Visualization*, Shakti Gawain describes visualization as using mental imagery and affirmations to create the life that you want.

There was another way that I explored visualization, apart from looking at the toys and projecting myself into the future when my child would play with them. Every day, I lay down on my back, closed my eyes, and listened to the song "Somewhere Over the Rainbow"—the beautiful Hawaiian version sung by Israel Kamakawiwo'ole. That song has always made me feel like everything good can happen. As I listened to the song, I would daydream. I saw myself dancing with my child, I would feel how it felt to be holding hands. I was overflowing with joy and with love in these dream sequences. We were both like lights dancing in the sky, delighted to be together. My husband would join us too, and the three of us would dance as lights in a dark sky.

I spoke to myself about being a mom—about how much I loved it, about how happy I was, about how grateful I was to be on the other side. I also pretended that I was on the other side of it, in the future, and wrote letters of thanks for my dream coming true. I wrote about how happy I was now that I was the mother of a beautiful healthy baby, and I wrote thank-yous for all the blessings that I had received by becoming a mom. I carefully put these letters in my God box or Higher Self Box—my box where my most cherished dreams and thank-yous are kept.

During these times, I felt and spoke to myself like it had already come to pass, that I was already a mother, that I was on the other side of this journey. I would imagine myself holding my baby in my arms and feel such a flow of love, joy, gratitude, and wonder. I let myself feel it in a huge, huge way! I took time every day to go into these feelings.

**My self-talk**
- I am so happy now that I am a mom.
- I love my baby so much.
- I am so lucky!!!
- What a blessing! Thank you! Thank you! Thank you!

**Time for reflection**
I invite you now to try a visualization daydream.

Sit quietly. Take deep breaths. Close your eyes. Imagine that you are on the other side of your fertility journey.

In your arms, you are holding a beautiful, healthy baby. Hold your arms up like you are holding that baby. Now let yourself feel it. How relieved you are. How joyful. How lucky! Feel a deep gratitude for this infant. Feel the love that you have. Look down into your baby's face, into your baby's eyes. Love this little being and yourself with all your heart. Tell yourself how lucky you are! Tell yourself how much you love this baby. Tell yourself about how much gratitude you feel.

# Chapter 14

# Be Brave!
## Choose self-talk for courage

The fertility journey takes a lot of courage. I never wanted to give up, but many times I was very scared. I was scared it would not happen for me. Scared of what I would become if it didn't. I was fearful that I couldn't handle another miscarriage, another disappointment. When my negative, critical voices were left to run the show in my head, I felt a lot more scared, and I was a lot more anxious.

Sometimes I underestimated my own ability to handle failure or disappointment. I underestimated just how courageous I was.

On one hand, I had courage, and on the other, I had fear. I learned that they are not mutually exclusive of each other. In fact, the more fear showed up, the more I had to summon courage.

A few years ago, I was just outside of Nice, France, on the evening a man drove his truck into fireworks revellers on the Promenade des Anglais. The next morning, I could see that this latest attack had scared and shaken the French. I also saw strangers reminding each other to have courage. They didn't say that there was nothing to fear, they said that courage was needed in a time like this.

I remind myself to have courage when I am scared. With more courage, I feel more calm, more accepting of circumstances, and more capable of facing them. I stand taller.

With courage, we can continue on our path until its natural conclusion, no matter where it leads.

**My self-talk**

- I see you are scared. I understand.
- This is a scary time. I am here for you.
- Let's breathe, take time, calm down.
- Be courageous, my love.
- You are much stronger and braver than you realize at this point.
- You are very capable of handling adversity. You are strong.

**Time for reflection**
When you start feeling strong emotions like fear, you can talk to yourself in the third person. Speaking to yourself in the third person permits you to take some distance from the fearful or upset voices. Research shows that when you hear your name in the third person, you will think of yourself similarly to how you think of others, so it is not so personal anymore. You can more easily regulate your emotions, including your fear, by getting a little distance from them.

For example:
- Maryse is ok.

- Just breathe, Maryse. You are ok.
- Maryse can do this.
- Maryse is strong enough and capable enough to go through this.
- Maryse has loads of courage.
- Maryse is healthy, solid, and calm.

What message do you want yourself to know about fear and courage? I encourage you to write it to yourself in the third person.

# Chapter 15

# Lighten Your Own Load
## Choose self-talk of levity and gratitude

One very cold morning, I found myself zooming in my car with a sample bottle of sperm safely stowed under my pants, where it would stay warm on my way to the lab. I had been told that it had to be in the lab quite quickly, so I was driving a little faster than usual. Suddenly, I hit a patch of black ice. For a few instants, my car veered out of control and spun around into the oncoming lane, then came to a stop.

No one was coming. I was safe. I took a deep breath, and continued my journey to the lab, but much more slowly this time.

I was scared, and also super grateful that I wasn't hurt, that I was ok. I thought of how important my life is—more important, even, than making a baby. I thought of all that I was grateful for: my husband, my home, my health, even little things like my mom's cooking, flowers, swimming in the ocean.

I also had to crack up. This was a very serious situation, but I brought a little levity to it: imagine if I had died with a sample of sperm tucked into my pants! It would have been ironic and ridiculous, to say the least. It made me smile a little and brought some levity to the situation.

Levity is also about giving yourself permission to have fun, to do things that you enjoy or see people that please you. The benefits of fun, humour, and levity are so numerous and so easy to access.

What we say to ourselves is either life-affirming—bringing us more of the good stuff, like love, calm, kindness, humour, compassion—or life-denying—taking us further away from the good stuff. Gratitude and levity help us to choose self-talk that is life-affirming. They elevate us, help us rise. They help us turn towards the light just like plants do on the window sill. As soon as you choose levity or gratitude, a joyous part of you shows up for this better time. What relief!

**My self-talk**
- Let's be a little lighter about this.
- Let's have a little fun. What would please you?
- What will bring you a little joy?
- Who would you like to see that makes you feel good?
- What can be funny about this?
- It is ok for you to be light and silly and to find humour everywhere you can.
- Life is such a gift, and life wants us to enjoy that gift to the max. Laugh, my love, laugh.
- You are my funny girl. I love you even when you are all worked up.

**A time for reflection**

I know that this journey is not especially funny. There were days when I found my journey exceptionally tragic. But is there any way you can lighten up the load you are carrying? Giving ourselves levity, humour, and gratitude are wonderful gifts, as they help us cope. We can do that with our self-talk.

Is there anything about it that can be comical? Amusing? Ironic? Even strange? What can you say that will bring a little levity to the way you talk to yourself about it? Is there anything that is funny about the way you are handling some situations?

Take a few moments here to see if you can lighten your load.

# Marie's Story

Marie MacDougal is now mom to healthy and happy 6-year-old twins. Here is her story and her words for you:

I stopped taking contraceptives at 30. At 38, I had everything checked. They couldn't find a reason why I wasn't getting pregnant. They told me it was stress, I needed to relax, to stop thinking of it. At 38, I really wanted to get pregnant and soon, but without a serious partner in my life, I didn't consider going to a fertility clinic. I wish I had. Once I did go, it took me five years of non-stop treatments at fertility clinics before my medical inability was detected. Once identified, right away I could carry a pregnancy to term.

Apparently, some women are able to stop wanting kids, but all those years, I couldn't. When family and friends urged me to move on with my life, I couldn't. I really wanted to be a mom. Key phrases I wish I had chosen at the beginning of this journey as my motto for this time: "Keep going," and "Giving up will not get you what you want."

I wish I had the medical knowledge of an expert in fertility and had been introduced to all current research being conducted worldwide on fertility issues. I wish there was one single place where all this information was being gathered, and where every woman with fertility issues could easily access.

I wish also I had had a support group of women who were going through treatments at fertility clinics like me. They are the only women who can really help you emotionally through this hard phase of your life. Forget about your mother, your sisters, or even your best friends, as they don't really understand. They will all at one point or another frustrate you, or even hurt you, with their comments.

I wish I had allowed myself a short vacation, even if just a long weekend away, somewhere memorable, to a different destination after each failed fertility treatment. It would be a way to thank myself for the efforts made even though a pregnancy was not achieved. I was so good making all those efforts and I wish I had thanked myself. I would set aside a budget for that and accept it as part of the overall costs of that specific fertility treatment.

# Chapter 16

## Getting to Know You
### Take the time to gently listen to your inner voice

When I was 15 years old, my father was transferred to Greece for his work. Our family packed up the house where we had always lived, and within weeks we were in Athens. I had never even travelled overseas before. This experience changed my life forever.

The Greeks do many things very well, and one of those is that they take the time to connect with their friends and family every day. No day is too busy to take the time to share a coffee and stories with your people. It is never complicated: something to drink, a little table and chairs, and voila—you connect.

At the international high school that I attended, I met my friend Mary, a beautiful, smart, humorous, and vibrant Greek from New York. Mary taught me the art of sharing stories and listening. Our friendship was built brick by brick, one story at a time, first in Greece, then in the many countries and cities where we visited each other over the years. We listened to each other's stories—the good ones, the sad ones, the humiliating ones, the super funny ones. We built trust and our stories became deeper, more personal. Some stories, I kept safely tucked away until I could sit with Mary somewhere in the world. I knew she would really listen to me.

She earned my trust because she listened and honoured what I said. She didn't use my stories against me.

This is how I learned to really listen to someone. My fertility journey was the time when I started building the relationship with myself, and I applied what my friend Mary taught me. I began spending quiet time with myself—just me and me, no distractions, asking myself questions and listening for answers. I tried to be as kind as I could about what I heard. I tried to show myself as much gentleness and understanding as I could—just like Mary does.

This was a huge turning point for me. I had lived most of my life before then disembodied, not really living within myself. I could go long periods of time without paying any attention to myself. I gave myself attention only if I was sick. I didn't know who I was, how I felt, or why I made decisions or acted in certain ways. I could not have told you what my self-talk was. I didn't listen to myself. I didn't ask questions.

I was a complete stranger to myself. I treated myself like someone you avoid at all costs. Imagine if you came to spend the evening with a friend and all they did was ignore you by using distractions. That's what I did every day. I did everything I could to blot my self-talk out: outings, friends, wine, music, books, movies. I didn't know that it was an option to have a good relationship with myself. I certainly didn't know that I could speak to myself in a way that would make me feel loved, connected, wanted, and good. I didn't know that all of that was in my power.

**My self-talk**

- I will listen to you now.
- I want to know how you feel.
- It's important to me to spend time with you.
- I am taking the time and space to be with you.
- I really enjoy our time together and getting to know you better.
- What a treat to be with you, my love!

**A time for reflection**

I start the Greek get-together by sitting. I try to focus on myself, to be fully present—like I would with a friend. Then I ask some questions—like I would with a friend. I ask myself what needs to be asked on that day. Questions like:

- How are you today?
- Is there anything you want me to know?
- What bothers you?
- Why are you sad?
- Why are you anxious?
- What is scaring you?
- Who do you miss?
- What do you need today?
- What needs to change?
- Is there anything I can do to help you feel better?

After I ask a question, I listen for an answer. Sometimes, my heart leaps. "Yes, you have hit the nail on the head," it says. "That is what is bothering me." Sometimes, there is no answer and nothing to know, nothing that I need to share with myself about that topic. "That is the truth, at least for now."

Whatever the answer is, I take a few moments to sit with it, to acknowledge it, just like I would if a friend shared something important, something from the heart.

Sometimes, I ask the questions verbally inside, other times, I write them down, and then write the answers that come to me.

Sit down quietly with yourself in a space where you will not be interrupted. Show yourself that it is important to you to get together with yourself. Pick a spot that you like. Bring a cup of tea. Take a deep breath and center yourself. Now ask yourself some questions, one at a time, and listen for an answer. You can do it in writing or in your heart.

# Chapter 17

## A Lotus Blooming in the Mud
### Choose self-talk for comfort on those hard days

Let's face it: Some days are arduous, even devastating. The days your period comes back, sending your hope crashing, visits to yet another doctor, painful interventions and tests, hormones—not to mention the nightmare of miscarriages. Then there are all of those strong emotions to deal with, like sadness, fear, anger, resentment, jealousy, disappointment, and shame.

It all took its toll on me. It was a very dark and rainy November day when I hit bottom. I became so sad and depressed that I feared I would enter a dangerous zone that I would not be able to climb back out of, no matter what the outcome.

I became scared that I would be an angry, resentful, hurt person my whole life. I came to believe that even when I had a child, it wouldn't solve how I felt inside. And what if I didn't become a mother—what then? I would still have to go on, and I didn't want to go on miserably.

I told myself that I would find a way out of this, that I would find a way to heal. I didn't know what it would look like, but I vowed that I would find a way to live with less suffering. I didn't know where to turn, but I started looking.

Very soon, I had the good fortune to listen to Oprah interviewing Elizabeth Lesser about her book *Broken Open: How Difficult Times Can Help Us Grow*. Something in that interview spoke to me, and I rushed out to get the book. It changed my life forever. In the book, Elizabeth writes about difficult times and how we can be broken open by them, like a flower that is forced to bloom open. Think of the lotus, blooming in the mud.

In her book, Elizabeth gives three pieces of advice to help us bloom through adversity: meditation, prayer, and therapy. I took up all three practices like my life depended on them—and maybe it did. All three are contemplative practices and not about action or movement. I had always walked—or run—away from my problems in the past. I didn't know anything about exploring them and sitting still with them, so I went looking for kind and experienced individuals who could teach me and guide me.

The first was my therapist. I met with him every week, and he guided me through one of the most difficult periods of my life. He encouraged me to keep a journal and to start building a relationship with myself. For the first time, I asked myself questions. I wrote down answers. I sat quietly with myself and just listened. I shared stories with my therapist and dug deeper. I discovered in myself a space that is peaceful, that I didn't know was there.

The second practice was meditation, and I found a teacher. Hoben is a solid teacher who has been practicing Zen meditation for decades. He showed me how to sit still and look for stillness inside, and to have the discipline to stay seated even when it becomes uncomfortable emotionally and physically.

Prayer came a little easier to me. I was raised Catholic, and even though I never did practice, I knew how to pray. I discovered that you can make up your own prayers, and I discovered the most important prayer of all: gratitude and thank-yous for all you have in your life. I prayed for help, guidance, strength, courage, and energy. When my good friend Erez, in Israel, said that he had gone to the Wailing Wall to insert a prayer on my behalf, I was so grateful, so touched. I would have welcomed prayers from all faiths to help me become a mom.

Through these three practices of meditation, therapy, and prayer, I began building a relationship with myself. I started practicing a very different kind of self-talk. I started trusting myself more. I started giving myself more love and care. I realized how worthy I was of it.

You are not meant to be a vessel that holds all the pain you have suffered—at your own hands, at the hand of others, and through life. You are not meant to be a museum of dark rooms dedicated to disappointments, anger, sadness, and old dusty stories that don't serve you. I had become such a museum, and what I did was open the windows wide open, let some light into the rooms, empty some of them out, give them a good spring cleaning, and reclaim some of the treasures buried in them. I'm still doing that.

I also developed ways of coping with hard days, such as taking hot baths, walking by the ocean, and spending time alone recharging and calming down.

For the first time in my life, I felt calm inside. I had a budding sense of how precious I was, no matter what the outcome of my journey. My relationship with myself became important to me, and I started nurturing it.

I am so grateful today for that book, for my meditation teacher, and for my therapist. I was transformed so profoundly that I was never the same after that. I am also grateful to my past self for doing the work so that I could know another way to be and to live.

## My self-talk
- I will find a way to help you.
- I am here for you. It will be all right.
- I will never leave you, no matter what.
- You are more important to me than everything else.
- This journey is so hard at times. We will find a way through it together.
- I trust you.

## A time for reflection
I invite you here to prepare a message for yourself, one that is from you to you. This message will help you on hard days, giving you love, compassion, support, and guidance.

Write the message and put in an envelope with your name on it. Underneath your name, write: *To open on a hard day*. You can also read the message to yourself and audio-record it on your phone to listen to on a hard day.

On this message:
- Write a sentence that acknowledges how hard it is and how you feel.
- Write a sentence of encouragement.
- Write a sentence to remind yourself that this will pass. You will not always be on this journey.
- Tell yourself about things that make you feel better.
- Write a sentence of compassion.
- Write about the things that help you feel better: (bath, visiting with a friend, buying flowers).
- Sign off with love.

Here is an example:

My Maryse,

I know how hard this is for you. I know how much you are suffering. I know how sad and scared you feel. Your feelings are normal for a woman going through what you are going through. I give you permission to feel your feelings. You don't have to pretend.

I know how much you want to be a mom. I am here for you.

You know this will pass, too. You have gotten through these feelings before. This is just a hard moment.

Remember that there are some things you can do to feel a little better. I give you permission to fully care for yourself. You can have a hot bath. You can sleep. You can drink warm tea. You can get in your pyjamas and rest and forget all that you have on your to-do list. You can practice deep breathing. You can take a walk by the ocean or go for a swim.

You also have a lot of help around you and I invite you to reach out when you feel like you need support.

Remember also how precious you are. I love you very much.

# Zaira's Story

Zaira Herrera is now mom to a healthy and happy 8-year-old boy. Here is her story and her words for you:

Before giving birth to my son, I tried five years in a row and had three miscarriages before 12 weeks and one miscarriage at 16 weeks, which was the most horrible of all.

It is hard to get pregnant and then lose the baby. I wish I had known how to talk to myself and be peaceful, and just keep trying until it finally happened.

Fertility problems change you. They make you feel less valuable in a weird sense. I knew I was worthy, but my body felt like a failure. The feeling of not being able to carry a pregnancy to term like everybody else crushed me.

I wish I had the wisdom to focus on doing other things, and not put my life on hold trying to make something happen that I had no control over.

I always wanted to become a yoga instructor, and I didn't do it because of "What if I am pregnant?" I was so focused on trying to be a mom. Don't take me wrong, the focus was important, but my life depended on my next menstrual cycle. It is heartbreaking, and is a time of uncertainty.

Even when I was pregnant with my son, it was a very stressful time, taking time off work, being in bed rest. My son was very premature. He is a miracle that I am grateful for every day.

My faith played a very important role in all this. I always prayed that God will make it happen, or give me resignation and understanding. At times I was angry because it wasn't happening when I wanted it to happen, but later on I understood that God had the perfect little boy for me, happy as he can be.

For all the women out there who are struggling with fertility, I want you to know that you are not alone. Don't isolate yourself. You are worthy. You are valuable. You are beautiful. You are healthy.

I am sure God has your little miracle in line for when is your time... the right time.

# Chapter 18

# The Dark Days of a Miscarriage
## Choose self-talk for tenderness and care

Miscarriages can be traumatic on so many levels: the grief, the shame, the fear, the physical and emotional suffering, the feeling of being alone in your pain as you may be told it is common and no big deal. It is possible to use your self-talk to help get yourself through it, to be there for yourself, and to hold your own hand.

It is said that the amount of emotional pain you feel with a miscarriage depends on the meaning you gave to the pregnancy and to its loss. Some women have reported still being sad decades after a miscarriage. Research shows that the duration of the pregnancy has nothing to do with how deep your grief is; it all has to do with what the pregnancy meant to you. A miscarriage can be much harder on some women than on others.

Miscarriages seem to be stored in a deep dark place and never be spoken of again, like they are shameful, or just too painful to discuss.

To me, my miscarriage was a huge deal. It plunged me into a dark night of the soul. It changed my life. True, it was part of my overall journey to motherhood, but it was so powerful that in some ways it stands apart. For me, the end of the pregnancy was a confirmation that I didn't merit what other women had, that there was something wrong with me, and that I wasn't worthy of becoming a mother. I also feared that there was something wrong with my body. I felt terribly alone, as I didn't know anyone who felt the same way about her miscarriage as I did.

After I miscarried, I spent three days in bed either crying or reading a novel. As soon as I stopped reading, I would cry again hard. I took sleeping aids to get to sleep. I didn't want to feel it. I didn't know how to live through something like this, so I just waited until I stopped crying and then soldiered on as I had always done. I stuffed that miscarriage down where I had put all my other pain and kept going.

I didn't know how to help myself through it. I didn't know how to sit by my own sickbed and hold my hand. I just wanted to get on with things as quickly as possible. I thought that if I felt my feelings, it would just make me sadder. As a consequence, I carried the grief and pain with me for years.

If I could go back in time, I would give myself all the time and space I needed to grieve and heal. I would shower myself with compassion. I would be gentle and kind to myself and to my body because what we were going through was traumatic. I would use my self-talk to get myself through that dark time.

This is what I wish I had said to myself:

- I love you. I love you. I love you.

- I am here for you and I will care for you.

- I can see that you are in so much pain. This is not your fault in any way.

- You can take all the time that you need to grieve.

- This is important. Normal life must wait.

- I know how much you love this baby and what this pregnancy meant to you.

- I will take care of everything. You can take the time to rest.

- Feeling my grief and other feelings of loss will help me heal.

- I will not pretend that everything is ok. I will honour myself through this.

- It does not matter what others say. They don't understand what this means for you.

- This will pass. I promise you, my love, this will pass.

- You are not alone. Many other women have lost their babies and feel the same way you do.

- If you need help, I will get it for you. We can get help to heal.

- There is no shame at all in grieving for someone you love. It is normal.

- Be gentle with yourself and with your body. You are going through a lot.

- Everything is going to be all right, one way or the other.

- I love you. I love you. I love you.


**A time for reflection**

I dragged myself around for a long time after the miscarriage. I carried that pain deep inside me for the baby that I lost. One day, years later, one of my teachers recommended that I write a letter to the self that had the miscarriage, offering myself compassion and love for the very hard time I had gone through.

In this letter I wrote that I understood how hard things were for me, how much I grieved, how I was scared that I would never be a mom. I showed myself that I understood. I held my own hand. After I wrote the letter, I read it to myself. Part of me felt a big relief at having been understood and at having someone connect with me. I was no longer alone.

I invite you here to write your own letter, if you are inspired. Fill it with understanding, love, and compassion, just like you would in a letter to your own daughter who had suffered a miscarriage.

# Chapter 19

# Your Support Person as the Wind in Your Sails
## Choose self-talk that gives you permission to open up
## and ask for help

The roller-coaster of the fertility journey is easier to endure if you have a support person. That person can be anyone who shows up for you and cares for you: your partner, a friend, a family member, or a professional that you trust. Every woman needs help during the fertility journey—a little or, in my case, a lot.

I was not used to letting other people see my vulnerability, to see me when I was low. There's a lot that I kept from the people I loved, including my husband. It was also very hard for me to ask for help. I had been doing it all on my own since I was young.

I remember a stretch of a few weeks that were particularly hard. I was going to therapy every week, and we were doing some deep work. I felt raw and emotional all the time. My therapist asked if I had been sharing all this with my husband, and I said no.

"He's very busy at work right now. I don't want to bother him," I answered.

That was true, but it wasn't the whole story. I didn't want to show him how low I was. The long years of the fertility journey had taken a toll, and I was still reeling from the miscarriage. Outside I kept a brave, optimistic face, teaching at the university, seeing friends. But inside, I was barely hanging on.

Keeping my most intense feelings buried inside didn't help. I know now that it only makes them more extreme. It's like trying to keep a beach ball under water. At some point, it comes crashing out.

My therapist persuaded me to talk to my husband without delay that very evening. When he came home from work, things got really real, as they say. After telling my husband just how I felt, I cried for hours. He held me for hours. We just stayed there together. After, I felt like a burden had been lifted. I also felt much closer to him, I trusted him more, and I began to lean on him more.

I remained the leader in our quest to become parents, doing the research, making the appointments, steering us in new directions when needed. But he became a stronger support person, more present. He provided strength through the losses. He was also there for our hopeful days.

I began using my self-talk to give myself permission to open up to him, to be more vulnerable, to share my true feelings, and to ask for help when I needed it.

**My self-talk**

- It is ok for me to ask for help.
- I give myself permission to tell the truth about how I feel. It doesn't make me any less strong.
- It is healthy and beneficial for me to share my feelings.
- I am not alone.

**A time for reflection**

Take a few moments to become clear on what you want and need from your support person. Are you getting the help that you need? Are you being real about how you feel? How can your support person best help you—mind, body and spirit—during this time?

If you don't have a support person presently, would you like to invite someone to play this meaningful role in your life?

# Words of support from

## Dr. Laura Von Hagen, naturopath

Dr. Laura von Hagen, M.Sc., ND, is a naturopathic doctor, with a focus in fertility. I had the opportunity to speak with her about the work she does with women longing to be mothers. What came out strongest was how much she loves her work and feels honoured to be helping women in this most precious of all endeavours. Here are Laura's words:

I am lucky to get to spend so much time with my patients. They tell me their stories. I get to know them well.

I go with my patients to fertility clinics to assist them by providing support and acupuncture before and after IVF. I am a safe place for them, a space where they won't get judged. I provide mental and emotional support.

This is so important because it is so stressful for women to be going through this. They feel so much is on the line, so much money.

The rates of depression and anxiety are the same as for women who have a chronic debilitating disease like cancer or HIV.

Some women also self-blame. They say it is their fault that they are not getting pregnant.

Some feel guilty for not trying earlier. There is a lot of ageism that is thrown at women. For instance, they may go to a fertility doctor and be told that they have few eggs because they are older.

There's lots of regret, and some women tell themselves "I wish I had…" kind of thing. That's one thing you can't do anything about. You can't change the past.

I say, yes, age is a factor, but let's focus on what we can control. There is still time to impact the quality of your eggs. Let's focus on the eggs you do have and their quality.

There is no room for judgement, I tell patients. Let's focus on the things we can change and have a healthy baby.

It's important, too, that women find ways to cope. I ask them, "What do you enjoy for fun and play right now?"

Women need to know: You are ok. You are trying as best as you can. It is possible. It does work. There is light on the other side. Acknowledge how hard you are working.

Please be kind to yourself and continue moving forward. These women are my most motivated and hard-working patients. I love them so much.

# Chapter 20

## It Is Possible
### Choose self-talk that enables hope and perseverance

I tell myself all the time that it's possible, about all kinds of things. Other people have managed, or have been lucky, so why not me?

As a little child, I wanted to travel, but our family didn't travel. I didn't even know anyone who travelled. When I was 15, I found out about high school exchange programs. I brought home brochures. I came really close to applying for one. Then my father said he just couldn't bear the idea of my leaving home for so long. "You will be gone quickly enough," he said. "These are our last years together."

Let me tell you what happened next. Within a few months, my father was promoted and, out of the blue, was offered a position based in Athens, Greece. We were gone within weeks and my life of travel began. I went from living in a boring (to a teenager, at least) suburb of Montreal to living in an exciting capital. From our home on the mountain, we could see all the way to the Acropolis.

This showed me that in life, everything is possible. It may not come like you expected, or look like your dreams, but the essence of it may come to you. I tell myself "It is possible" all the time, no matter what the odds are, no matter if I have no idea how something can come to be.

At my first meeting at a fertility clinic, the doctor told me that my chances of getting pregnant were less than five percent. I breathed a sigh of relief. What I heard is: It is possible! I had started to believe that it was not possible, but here was someone telling me that it was. It was possible! It could happen, and from then on, I would leave no stone unturned in my pursuit of this possibility.

The fertility journey asks us for hope, but it also asks us for perseverance. It can be a physically and emotionally taxing process, that is for sure. A certain amount of grit is needed. It is about keeping it up step after step, little by little, slowly, slowly, day after day.

In the book *A Few Good Eggs: Two Chicks Dish on Overcoming the Insanity of Infertility*, the two authors, who became moms after their own journeys, write that if you don't give up, you will become a mother somehow. It may not look like you thought, or happen like you thought, but it will happen.

My meditation teacher, Hoben, says that we need to have faith in ourselves and to have a fire in our belly—a strong desire to keep going even when times are tough.

My friend had a baby after trying for over 10 years. What perseverance that took! Becoming a mom looked entirely different from what she first imagined. Donor eggs were the miracle that worked for her.

Perseverance is not blindly going in the same direction and doing the same thing, no matter what is going on. It is about being strategic, looking at different options, knowing when it is time to move to your plan B, or plan C, or plan D. Step by step, day by day.

When I lived in Japan, I learned the expression "Gannbate kudasai." It means "Please do your best," "Keep it up," or "Hang in there." That is what I say to you, my sweet one, during this journey: Gannbate kudasai!

**My self-talk**
- It is possible.
- It can happen for me.
- I can become a mom.
- So many other women have been in my shoes and become mothers.
- Why not me?
- There is so much abundance in this world.
- I am resilient.
- I have a fierce determination, a fire in my belly. I keep it up.
- It's ok, take a deep breath.
- Step by step. Slowly, slowly.

**A time for reflection**
What does it mean for you to have hope and to persevere? Tell yourself about it. Is there an example from your own life where hope and perseverance were key?

# A Million Thank Yous

- I am most grateful for the opportunity to be my daughter's mother. She shows me what love is every day. Thank you for coming, my sweet girl.

- My husband is still my support person extraordinaire. Thank you for your steadfastness and love.

- To all the brave, wonderful women who shared their stories with me: You inspire me with your courage, endurance, and love. May your stories help our Sisters become moms too. Thank you Zaira, Michelle, Laila, Marie.

- Thank you Dr Alda, acupuncturist, for sharing your story and your wisdom.

- Thank you Dr Laura, naturopath, for sharing your wisdom and your love for all women on the fertility path.

- To all the professionals who helped me on my way: to my doctors, acupuncturists, yoga and meditation teachers, my therapist, the authors of books that inspired me: All of you kept the wind blowing in my sails, and helped me become a mom. What you do is so precious. I am thankful for the help and expertise you gave me.

- Thank you to the women who blog about their own fertility issues, helping all of us with their vulnerability and openness about their truth.

- Thank you Avital for the beautiful book cover design. It means a lot to me.

- Thank you Sara for bringing your editing gusto to my manuscript once more.

- Thank you to the Divine for my life. I am so grateful to be living.

# About the Author

Maryse Cardin is an author, workshop leader, university teacher, communications practitioner, and coach. She is dedicated to speaking to herself with love, compassion, and kindness, and to helping others learn to do the same. Her passion for teaching positive and loving self-talk is driven by her desire for everyone to have lives filled with love, health, calm, joy, and fulfilment. She has a special place in her heart for all women on the fertility journey. She lives with her family in Vancouver. Find out more about Maryse, her books, workshops and webinars, at www.selftalklove.com                              and www.facebook.com/selftalklove.

Made in the USA
Monee, IL
12 April 2022